David Fickling Books

Max & Chaffy
in
The Great Cupcake Mystery!

Far, far across the ocean
there is an island . . .

And on that island
is a lighthouse . . .

And inside that lighthouse, MAX and CHAFFY are just waking up!

8

9

10

11

20

21

That is our special guest!

The entertainer for the party...

DJ MOLEY MOLE!

Well, maybe Chaffy and I can solve this mystery?

Meep!

Let's think. What would Chief Constable Moose do?

Umm.

Err.

He'd have a nap?

No, he'd look for clues!

The Rock Pools!

Nope.

Since the trail of candles ends here, maybe there's another clue to find, Chaffy!

Meep!

The Sunny
Meadows!

49

We're still looking for the missing cupcake!

neeeyow

HappyBirthday!

What ho, Max and Chaffy! I'm just testing out my birthday banner!

The Caves!

And I'm delivering an invitation to the birthday party, as a way of saying thank you!

Come to a Party!

To: The Glow-worms
In the caves
On Animal Island

They've said they're free and they can come!

Hooray!

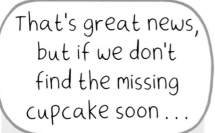

70

DJ Moley Mole's Holey Hole!

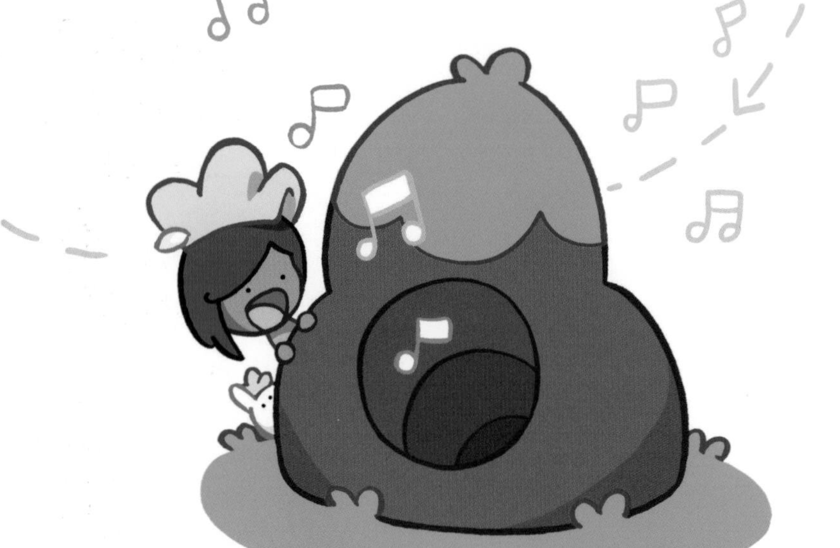

I noticed you have mole holes all over Animal Island!

I wondered if a clue to the missing cupcake might have fallen into one of them.

There we go, Chaffy. We both look like real detectives now!

Meep!

But this hat feels a bit . . . ITCHY!

scratch scratch!

I didn't realise there was **ANOTHER** chaffy on Animal Island!

And it's wearing a hat, just like Chief Constable Moose!

IDEA!

Maybe **THIS** chaffy could help us find the missing cupcake?

Meep!

Pheep!

95

And more.
And MORE.

And now I have a TUMMY ACHE!

Goodness me, I'm seeing things too. There are TWO chaffies?

The Birthday Party!

But, **CRUMBLES**, you made the cupcake **FOR** Chief Constable Moose!

I did, didn't I!

And it was **DELICIOUS!**

I'm so glad!

I was trying so hard to make the party perfect, I ended up ignoring you on your big day!

. . . and I asked this chaffy to join me doing my police work.
Please say hello to . . .
. . . DEPUTY CONSTABLE CHAFFY!
Pheep pheep pheep!

But wait!
The search isn't over! Chief Constable Moose received a lot of birthday presents from his family, but ... well, I may have mislaid them around the island. Can **YOU** help me find them?

The Party

Blue Present

Framed Photo

Mummy

Yellow Present

The Rock Pools

Fish-shaped Present

Jumper

Green Present

Animal

Birthda

The Meadows

Flower

Birthday Voucher

Big Fork

The Caves

Roller Skates

Balloon

Bucket

DJ Moley Mole's

Purple Present

Orange Present

Birthday Card

Holey Hole

Island Map!

Answers this way!

Answers

Did you find all the presents? Oh, well done. Chief Constable Moose will be so happy!

The Party

Yellow Present

Framed Photo

Blue Present

The Rock Pools

Jumper

Green Present

Fish-shaped Present

The Meadows

Flower

Big Fork

Birthday Voucher

The Caves

Roller Skates

Bucket

Balloon

DJ Moley Mole's Holey Hole

Purple Present

Orange Present

Birthday Card

More adventures with
MAX & CHAFFY
OUT NOW!

More adventures with
MAX & CHAFFY
COMING SOON!

There's a whole world to explore...

FIND CHAFFY

Hi! I'm Jamie Smart.
I hope you loved reading about Max and Chaffy.
I really enjoyed writing and drawing it.
Thank you to my friends Emily, Rosie and Katie
who all helped me make this book too!
I've also created other books, like the best-selling

 and LOOSHKIN

Making up stories and looking for chaffies
are my two favourite things!